M and M and other stories

Compiled by Pat Edwards and Wendy Body

Acknowledgements

We are grateful to the following for permission to reproduce copyright material:
McIntosh and Otis Inc. for the story 'Say Hello, Vanessa' by Marjorie Weinman Sharmat
Copyright © 1979 by Marjorie Weinman Sharmat; Pantheon Books, a Division of
Random House, Inc. for an extract from *M and M and The Big Bag* by Pat Ross and
illustrated by Marylin Hafner Copyright © 1981 by Pat Ross and Marylin Hafner.
Illustrations to 'Say Hello, Vanessa' by Lillian Hoban Copyright © 1979 by permission
of Holiday House; illustrations to 'M and M Go Shopping' by Jill Brierley by
permission of Longman Cheshire Pty.

Illustrators, other than those acknowledged above, include: Robert Avitabile pp.26–27;
Linda Forss pp.46–47; Charles Front pp.48–61; Judy Nelson pp.28–29; Jill Ogilvy p.62.

TODAY'S SPECIALS

Contents

M and M
go shopping

CHAPTER ONE

Mandy and Mimi — the two friends who called themselves M and M — looked carefully at the yellow sheet of paper. The big black letters at the top spelled GROCERY LIST. But it was not just *any* grocery list. It was a very important grocery list. So they read it three times.

Mandy and Mimi were going to the grocery shop without a grown-up for the very first time. And the list was for them.

"This is it!" cried Mandy.

"It's about time!" cried Mimi.

The friends M and M were ready for this day. They could read prices and signs. They could even read tricky words like *cucumber* and *pizza*. They could count their change. And they always looked both ways before they crossed the street. They were ready all right — ready to shop at The Big Bag alone.

They looked at the grocery list again. The paper was clean and smooth. The words were big and neat.

They read the list one more time —

GROCERY LIST
1 butter
1 bread
2 apples
1 box rubbish bags
1 milk

"That's an easy list," said Mimi.

"Nothing to it," said Mandy.

Mandy was in charge of the list. She folded the paper and tucked it under her belt. Mimi was in charge of the money. She pushed a five-pound note deep into her back pocket. Then she wiggled and jumped to make sure the money was safe.

"OK, let's move it!" Mimi shouted.
Mimi's dog Maxi ran to the door and barked.
Maxi didn't want to be left behind.

"No Maxi," they said.

"You can't come."
But Maxi sat right by the door.

"OK, OK," said Mimi. "You win. But you'd
better be good. We're going to The Big
Bag!"

CHAPTER TWO

Mandy and Mimi had to cross two streets
to get to The Big Bag. One street was big
and wide. It had noisy buses and fast cars.
M and M waited for the green man light
before they crossed the street.

The Big Bag had two front doors. One said OUT and NO PUSHCHAIRS. The other said IN and NO DOGS ALLOWED.

"That means you," said Mimi to Maxi.

Maxi didn't like being left outside — not one bit! He started to bark.

"Be a good dog!" said Mandy, and she bent down to pat him.

Just then, a piece of paper — a piece of
yellow paper — fell on the pavement.
Mandy didn't see it fall. Mimi didn't see it
fall. But Maxi did. Maxi barked at the
paper.

"Come on," said Mimi.

"Maxi always makes a fuss. Just pretend
you don't know him."

So M and M turned away and they went
into The Big Bag.

CHAPTER THREE

"What's first on the list?" asked Mimi.
Mandy reached under her belt.

"It's gone!' she cried.

"What are we going to do?"

"Who needs that list anyway? We know
what to buy," said Mimi.

"Are you sure?" asked Mandy.
She wished they had the list.

"Yes, I'm sure," said Mimi. "I remember
everything."

"OK," said Mandy.
She hoped that was the truth.

The Big Bag looked bigger than ever. There were so many rows. There were so many signs. There was so much food.

They decided to start with the row that
said SNACKS.

"Was popcorn on the list?" asked Mimi.

"I thought you remembered everything,"
said Mandy.

"Well, I *think* it was on the list," said Mimi.
And she put popcorn in the trolley. Popcorn
was her favourite snack.

"What came after popcorn?" asked Mandy. Mimi looked at a row of soft drink.

"If soft drink was not on the list, it should have been," she said.

So Mandy put two bottles of soft drink in the trolley.

"Hey! What about that new cereal with the free aeroplane inside?" asked Mimi.

"Yeah," said Mandy. "Grown-ups like it when you try something new."

So Mimi put a box of Super Krunchy in the trolley.

Soon, the trolley was filled with
> popcorn,
> soft drink,
> cereal,
> peanut butter plain,
> peanut butter crunchy,
> chocolate ice cream,
> paper cups,
> tooth brushes, and
> grape bubble gum.

Mandy and Mimi got in line for the
check-out counter. They looked at the
trolley. It was loaded to the very top. They
looked at the five-pound note. Then
they looked at each other.

"We needed the list," said Mandy.

"I usually remember better," said Mimi.

"We'll never get to go shopping again if we come back with all this stuff!" cried Mandy.

"What do we do now?"

"Dump it," said Mimi.

"Dump it?" asked Mandy.

"Like this," said Mimi.

Quickly, Mimi pushed the trolley to the back of the store — and left it there.

They ran for the door that said OUT. And there was Maxi with a yellow something in his mouth.

"The list!" cried Mandy.

"Here Maxi," said Mimi.
Maxi chewed the paper.

"Nice Maxi," said Mimi.
Maxi still chewed the paper. Mimi took a dog treat out of her pocket. Maxi dropped the paper. Now the yellow list was wet and slimy, sticky and dirty. It had holes in it — little dog-tooth holes.

"You dropped it," said Mimi. "You pick it up."

"Yuck," said Mandy.

CHAPTER FOUR

M and M went back into The Big Bag with
the list. The list was smelly. And it ripped
when Mandy tried to smooth it out. Mandy
and Mimi looked at the first word and
laughed. It said

I butt

"Butter!" said Mandy.
And they ran to get one butter.

The next word on the list started with a
dog-tooth hole. Then came the letters

read

But that did not fool them! They knew the
word was BREAD.

apples was the only whole word. They
picked out two good ones.

The next word on the list was *rubbish*

"This is a shop, not a dump!" said Mandy.
Then they raced the trolley to rubbish bags.

The last word was all rubbed out. But Mandy and Mimi knew the word was not popcorn or soft drink. They knew the word was milk. And they picked out the coldest one.

"Well that's it," said M and M.
The man at the check-out counter rang up each thing.

"That comes to three pounds and forty pence," he said.
Mimi gave the clerk the five-pound note.
He gave her back one pound and sixty pence.

"Come again," said the man.

"Oh, we will!" they answered.

They ran outside and untied Maxi. Then they gave him the list.

"It's all yours now," said Mandy.
And Maxi chewed the list right up!

Then M and M took turns carrying one butter, one bread, two apples, rubbish bags, and one milk home without stopping.

Written by *Pat Ross*
Illustrated by *Jill Brierley*

How does it work?
The cash register

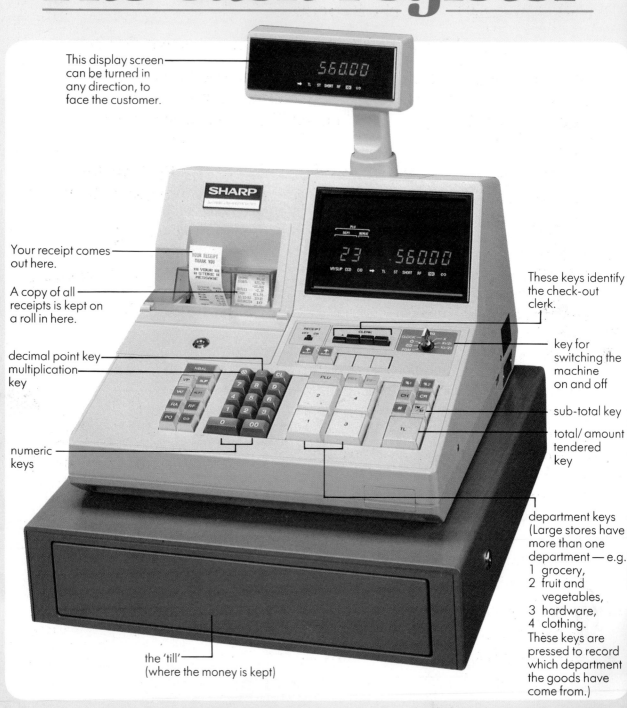

This display screen can be turned in any direction, to face the customer.

Your receipt comes out here.

A copy of all receipts is kept on a roll in here.

decimal point key
multiplication key

numeric keys

These keys identify the check-out clerk.

key for switching the machine on and off

sub-total key

total/ amount tendered key

department keys (Large stores have more than one department — e.g.
1 grocery,
2 fruit and vegetables,
3 hardware,
4 clothing.
These keys are pressed to record which department the goods have come from.)

the 'till' (where the money is kept)

Imagine that you are the check-out clerk at The Big Bag.
The prices of the things M and M are buying are:
butter 65 pence, bread 62 pence, apples 19 pence each,
rubbish bags £1.49, milk 26 pence.

If you were using this cash register, here's what you would do:

1   Ring up the prices by pressing the "numeric keys". For
butter you press ⬜6 ⬜5 . (The machine can put in the
decimal point for you.) Then press the "department key"
(e.g. ⬜1 grocery).

To show two apples, you press ⬜2 , then the multiplication
key ⊗ and finally ⬜1⬜9 . Then press the "department key"
(e.g. ⬜2 fruit and vegetables).

2   When all the prices have been
entered on the machine, you
press the "sub-total" key, to
get the total of Mimi's bill.
The machine will show £3.40,
on the screens.

3   When Mimi hands you the five
pounds, you press ⬜5 ⬜00 ,
then you press the "total/
amount tendered" key. (What
Mimi gives you is called "the
amount tendered".) The
machine works out the
change and £1.60 will show
on the screens. The
drawer now opens.

4   You give Mimi this change
and her receipt and then shut the
till, ready for the next customer.

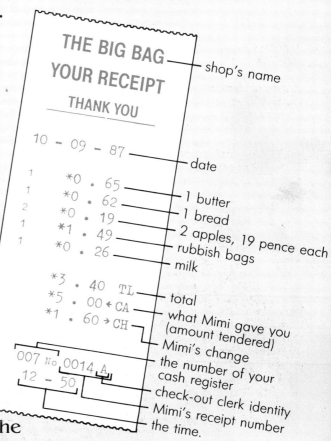

THE BIG BAG ———— shop's name
YOUR RECEIPT
THANK YOU
_____

10 - 09 - 87 ———— date

1   *0 . 65 ———— 1 butter
1   *0 . 62 ———— 1 bread
2   *0 . 19 ———— 2 apples, 19 pence each
1   *1 . 49 ———— rubbish bags
1   *0 . 26 ———— milk

*3 . 40   TL ———— total
*5 . 00 ← CA ———— what Mimi gave you (amount tendered)
*1 . 60 → CH ———— Mimi's change

007 No 0014 A ———— the number of your cash register
12 - 50 ———— check-out clerk identity
                    Mimi's receipt number
                    the time.

Where do we get it?
BREAD

Start at the top and read your way down the page, then back again.

wheat field and combine harvester

from silo to flour mill

wheat cleaned and washed

wheat is tempered: water is added to help separate the outer layer of each grain (the bran) from the inner part (the endosperm)

wheat is ground and sifted

fine flour packed and despatched to bakery

flour unloaded at the bakery

flour is mixed with yeast, water, salt and a little fat to make the dough

dough is allowed to "rise" for up to 5 hours

dough is cut to loaf sizes, by weight

pieces of dough are placed in baking pans and are allowed to rise for ½ – 1 hour. This is called "proofing"

bread is baked for 20–40 minutes

Shopping Don'ts

NO PETS ALLOWED

Don't take pets shopping.

Don't be careless with things that break.

Don't play on trolleys or run in aisles.

When food is stacked don't take the bottom tin or packet.

Don't put your hand on the side of a deep freeze.

Don't buy more than you can pay for.

Don't let your pet eat your list.

Say Hello, Vanessa

Vanessa Mouse lived with her mother and father on three floors of a fine, old house.

Mrs Mouse had many friends. When they came to visit, Vanessa hid under the sofa and peeked out.

"Say hello, Vanessa," said her mother. But Vanessa didn't.

When Mr Mouse's friends came over,
Vanessa sat in a corner and didn't look up.

"Look up, Vanessa," said her father.
But Vanessa wouldn't.

No friends came over to see Vanessa.
Because Vanessa didn't have any.

"Not one friend," said Mrs Mouse sadly.
"Not even a now-and-then friend. Or an every
Sunday friend. Or a rainy day, sit-by-the-
window-and-nibble-crumbs friend. Nobody."

"Trying to make friends must be the scariest
thing in the world," said Vanessa.

"Well, the first time might be a little scary,"
said Mrs Mouse. "But why don't you try it?"

The next day Vanessa went to school. She took her seat in class behind Quincy Moose.

"It's wonderful hiding here behind Quincy Moose's antlers," thought Vanessa.

Mr Mitchell, the teacher, said, "Today we'll start with spelling."

He looked at Andrew Aardvark. "Andrew, how do you spell country?"

"Does it begin with a *k*?" asked Andrew.

"No, I'm afraid it doesn't," said Mr Mitchell. He looked at Craig Badger. "Can you spell country, Craig?"

"Does it end with an *e*?" asked Craig.

"No," said Mr Mitchell, "it doesn't. Who knows how to spell country?"

Vanessa started to raise her hand. "I know how, I know how," she said to herself.

She lowered her hand. "But I can't. Everybody will look at me and my funny teeth and my furry face. Maybe I'll spell country tomorrow."

After class, everyone got together in little bunches and groups. Except Vanessa who was all alone.

"Bunches and groups, bunches and groups," thought Vanessa. "Everybody has enough friends already. They don't need me."

When she got home, her mother asked, "Well, Vanessa, did you make a friend today?"

"No," said Vanessa. And she told her mother about bunches and groups.

"I understand," said Mrs Mouse. "But if you look hard enough, you'll find someone who is alone. Then you can go up and say hello."

"I'll try that," said Vanessa.

At school the next morning, Mr Mitchell asked, "Who has learned to spell country?"

Everyone looked around.

"Here's a chance that might never come again," thought Vanessa.

Vanessa started to raise her hand. But she put it down again. "Maybe tomorrow I'll do it," she thought.

When class was over, Vanessa saw Lisa Goat standing alone against a wall.

Slowly Vanessa went up to Lisa. Then Vanessa whispered, "Hello."

"What?" asked Lisa.

"Hello," whispered Vanessa.

"What?" asked Lisa again.

HELLO.

Vanessa walked away.

She ran home to her mother. "I said hello but I didn't make a friend," said Vanessa.

"Saying hello usually works," said Mrs Mouse.

"It didn't for me," said Vanessa. "I went up to Lisa Goat very politely and said hello, just like that, but all she said was *what*?"

"Try again tomorrow with someone else," said Mrs Mouse. "And speak a little louder."

"I'll try," said Vanessa.

Vanessa hurried to school the next morning and took her seat behind Quincy Moose.

Mr Mitchell asked, "Who can spell country?"

"Me!" shouted Andrew Aardvark.

"I can, too," said Craig Badger.

"C-o-u-n-t-r-y!" someone else spelled.

"Nuts!" thought Vanessa. "Well, anyway, the day isn't over yet."

Vanessa walked up and down the hall looking for someone who was alone. At last she saw Sigmund Toad counting the pencils in his pencil pouch.

Vanessa walked up to him. **"HELLO!"** she shouted.

Sigmund dropped his pencil pouch.

"HELLO!" she shouted again.
Sigmund put his hands over his ears and hopped away.

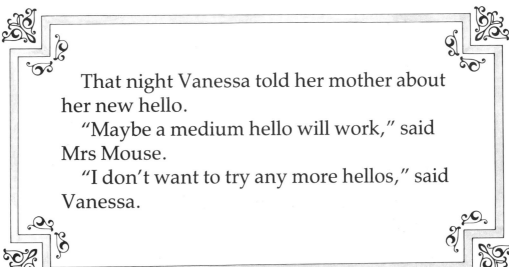

That night Vanessa told her mother about her new hello.

"Maybe a medium hello will work," said Mrs Mouse.

"I don't want to try any more hellos," said Vanessa.

The next day Vanessa's mind was made up. "Today I will not say anything. Not anything at all!" she said to herself.

She took her seat behind Quincy Moose.

"This morning we have a new word to spell, and it's a difficult one," said Mr Mitchell. "Does anyone know how to spell tooth?"

"Oh!" thought Vanessa. "I do! I know that word!"

Mr Mitchell looked around.

Andrew was squirming in his seat. Craig was pulling on his ear.

Vanessa felt hot and thumpy inside. She was thinking, "Tooth is such a great word to know how to spell, and *I* know how to spell it!"

Suddenly Vanessa raised her hand high. And higher. She wiggled it. She waved it. She said, "I can spell tooth! I can spell it! T-o-o-t-h!"

"Perfect," said Mr Mitchell.

Everyone was looking at Vanessa. But she didn't mind. In fact she felt good.

After class was over, Vanessa gathered up her books.

Suddenly Quincy Moose turned around, "I wish I knew how to spell tooth," he said. "I wish I knew how to spell moose."

"Moose is easy," said Vanessa. "It's like mouse except it has an *o* where the *u* is."

Vanessa and Quincy walked out of class together.

They sat on a bench and talked about *mouse* and *moose*.

"That was fun," said Quincy. "Let's do it again."

"Want to come to my house?" asked Vanessa.

"Sure," said Quincy.

Vanessa and Quincy walked to Vanessa's house. They passed Mr Mitchell.

"Hello, Mr Mitchell," said Vanessa.

They passed Andrew Aardvark.

"Hi there, Andrew," said Vanessa.

They passed Craig Badger.

"How are you, Craig?" said Vanessa.

They passed Lisa Goat.

"Greetings, Lisa," said Vanessa.

They passed Sigmund Toad.

"Nice day, Sigmund!" said Vanessa.

When Vanessa got home, she ran into the house.

"Mother! Mother! I brought someone home!"

"I'm Quincy Moose. M-o-o-s-e," said Quincy. "And you must be Mrs Mouse. M-o-u-s-e."

"And you must be Vanessa's friend," said Mrs Mouse.

"That's who I am!" said Quincy.

"A friend is fun to have," said Vanessa. "Especially an everyday, sit-by-the-fire-and-talk friend."

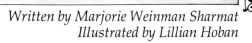

Written by Marjorie Weinman Sharmat
Illustrated by Lillian Hoban

I'm Shy

Whenever I meet people in the street I hang my head, wish I was dead, pretend I don't see when they wave to me. And then at school I feel a fool when teacher shows how, then says, "Well now, who understands?" Lots put up their hands, but even if I know, I sit really low or scrunch in my seat and look at my feet. I don't know why I'm shy.

BUT I HATE IT!

Pat Edwards

Why were you Shy Hans Christian Andersen?

WHO was Hans Christian Andersen?

He was a writer of fairy tales who lived in Denmark from 1805 until 1875.

THE STEADFAST TIN SOLDIER

WHY was he shy?

Hans was a very plain boy. He had a big nose and very large feet and a high squeaky voice. He thought people would laugh at him, so became a shy lonely man. People say that his story, The Ugly Duckling, is really about himself.

THE UGLY DUCKLING

WHAT did he write?

Mostly fairy tales for children. Best known stories are The Ugly Duckling, The Little Match Girl, The Emperor's New Clothes, The Steadfast Tin Soldier and The Tinder Box.

WHEN do we remember him?

On 2 April. This was Hans Christian Andersen's birthday, so the day was chosen as International Children's Book Day. It's when all writers for children are honoured.

THE LITTLE MATCH GIRL

THE EMPEROR'S NEW CLOTHES

The Tinder Box

Once upon a time a soldier was on his way home
from the war. He met a wicked-looking witch who
said to him:

"Do you want to be rich? Would you like as
much money as you can carry?"

"Yes, of course I would," said the soldier.
"What do I have to do?"

"That tree over there is hollow," said the witch. "Climb down inside it and you will find an underground passage lit by a hundred lamps. There are three rooms leading from this passage. In each room there is a chest of coins. The first chest is full of copper, the second is full of silver and the third is full of gold.

The copper is guarded by a dog with eyes as big as saucers. The silver is guarded by a dog with eyes as big as millstones. The gold is guarded by a dog with eyes as big as towers."

"But you need not worry about the dogs," the witch went on to say. "Just do as I tell you. Take my apron and when you go into each room put it on the ground. Then lift the dog off the chest and sit it on the apron. You will be able to take as many coins as you like and the dogs will not hurt you.

"That sounds easy," said the soldier. "Will you want to share the coins with me when I get back?"

"No, no," said the witch. "All I want is the tinder box that you will find down there. It belongs to my grandmother and she left it down there by mistake."

So the soldier climbed down inside the hollow tree. He found everything the way the witch had said it would be. He was nervous when he saw the three dogs with their huge great eyes. But he did as the witch had told him to and they did not hurt him.

The soldier came back to the witch with as much gold as he could carry – and the tinder box.

"Why do you want the tinder box?" he asked the witch.

"I shan't tell you," she replied rudely.

"Tell me or I shall chop off your head!" said the soldier.

"Shan't," screamed the witch.

51

The soldier pulled out his sword and chopped off the witch's head. Then he put all his gold coins in the witch's apron and threw the bundle on his back. Off he went to the nearest town carrying his money (AND the tinder box!).

The soldier enjoyed being rich and for a time he
lived a fine life. But before long his money was
spent and the soldier was poor again. He did not
even have enough money to buy a candle to light
his dark room. Then he remembered that there was
a candle stub in the tinder box.

The soldier struck the flint once to light the
candle. Suddenly the door burst open and in came
the dog with eyes as big as saucers.

"What is my master's wish?" it said.

"Fetch me some money!" cried the soldier.
Off went the dog and in no time at all it was back
with a bag of copper coins in its mouth.

Now the soldier knew why the witch had wanted
the tinder box. Strike the flint once and the dog
with eyes as big as saucers would appear. Two
strikes would bring the dog with eyes as big as
millstones and three strikes would bring the dog
that guarded the gold.

The soldier need never be poor again.

Now, in the town where the soldier lived there
was a copper palace that belonged to the king. The
king kept his daughter locked up in the palace
because he was afraid that she would marry a
common soldier. He didn't want that to happen,
oh no. He wanted her to marry a prince.

The soldier had heard about the princess and he
very much wanted to see her for himself. So one
night he struck the tinder box once and when the
dog with eyes as big as saucers appeared he said to it:

"I want to see the princess. Fetch her here to me."

In no time at all, the dog was back again carrying the princess on its back. She was fast asleep. The soldier looked at the sleeping princess. She was so beautiful that he kissed her. Then he told the dog to take her back to the copper palace.

The next morning, the princess told the king and queen about the dream she'd had. A big dog had carried her to a soldier who had kissed her.

The king and queen were worried. The next night when the dog came again they tried to find out where it was taking the princess. But the dog was too clever for them.

The soldier had fallen in love with the princess
and he wanted to marry her. On the third night he
sent the dog to fetch her once more. But the queen
had thought of a plan to find out where the
sleeping princess was being taken.

She had tied a little silk bag filled with flour
around her daughter's waist. Then she had made
a tiny hole in the bag.

Later that night the dog came to fetch the
sleeping princess and take her to the soldier's
home. But on the way, the flour trickled from the
bag and left a trail for the king and queen to follow.
The dog did not see the trail of flour leading to the
soldier's house.

When the guards arrived at the soldier's house he did not have time to pick up the tinder box. He was taken to prison and told that he would be hanged the next day.

As the sun rose, the soldier was looking out of the prison window. He saw a boy close by. The soldier called the boy over and paid him to fetch the tinder box for him.

The boy had not long returned with the box when the guards arrived. They took the soldier into the town square to be hanged.

They put the rope around his neck and then the
soldier cried out: ·

"Let me have one last pipe of tobacco before I die!"

The king agreed and so the soldier took out his
tinder box. He struck it once, twice, three times.

Suddenly all three dogs were at his side: the dog
with eyes as big as saucers, the dog with eyes as big
as millstones and the dog with eyes as big as towers.

"Help me!" the soldier shouted to the dogs.
All three dogs leapt upon the people in the
crowd. Everyone ran screaming until the king
cried out:

"Enough, you can marry my daughter, but
call off those dogs!"

And so the soldier and the princess were married. Hundreds of people came to the wedding feast which lasted for a week and a day.

The three dogs were at the feast too – keeping watch over their master and their new mistress: the dog with eyes as big as saucers, the dog with eyes as big as millstones and the dog with eyes as big as towers.

But did they all live happily ever after?

Adapted by Wendy Body from the story by Hans Christian Andersen
Illustrated by Charles Front

Eyes like saucers . . .?
Eyes like millstones . . .?
No! Eyes like this . . .

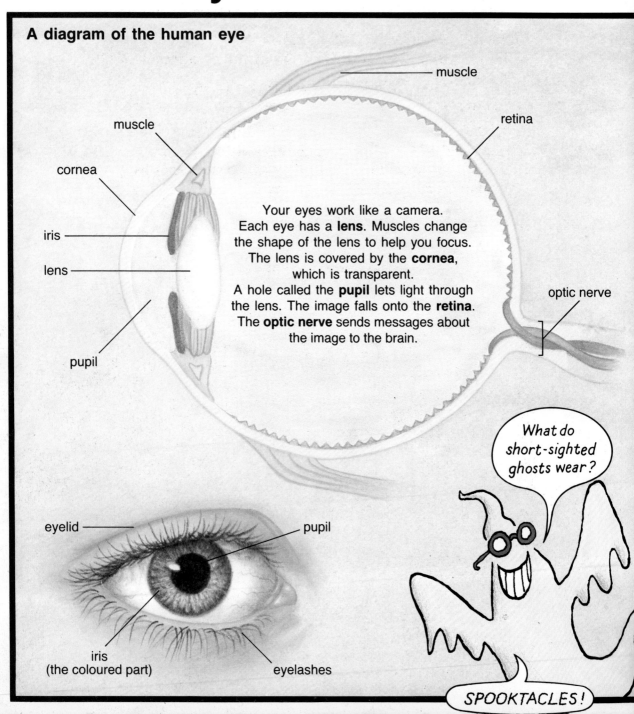

A diagram of the human eye

muscle

retina

muscle

cornea

iris

lens

Your eyes work like a camera.
Each eye has a **lens**. Muscles change
the shape of the lens to help you focus.
The lens is covered by the **cornea**,
which is transparent.
A hole called the **pupil** lets light through
the lens. The image falls onto the **retina**.
The **optic nerve** sends messages about
the image to the brain.

optic nerve

pupil

eyelid

pupil

iris
(the coloured part)

eyelashes

What do
short-sighted
ghosts wear?

SPOOKTACLES!